# DESMOND AT THE ZOO

story and pictures by Althea

ISBN 0-905-114-79-5 (paperback)
ISBN 0-905-114-85-X (hardback)

Published by Bridge Street Books
LDA Duke Street Wisbech Cambridgeshire PE13 2AE

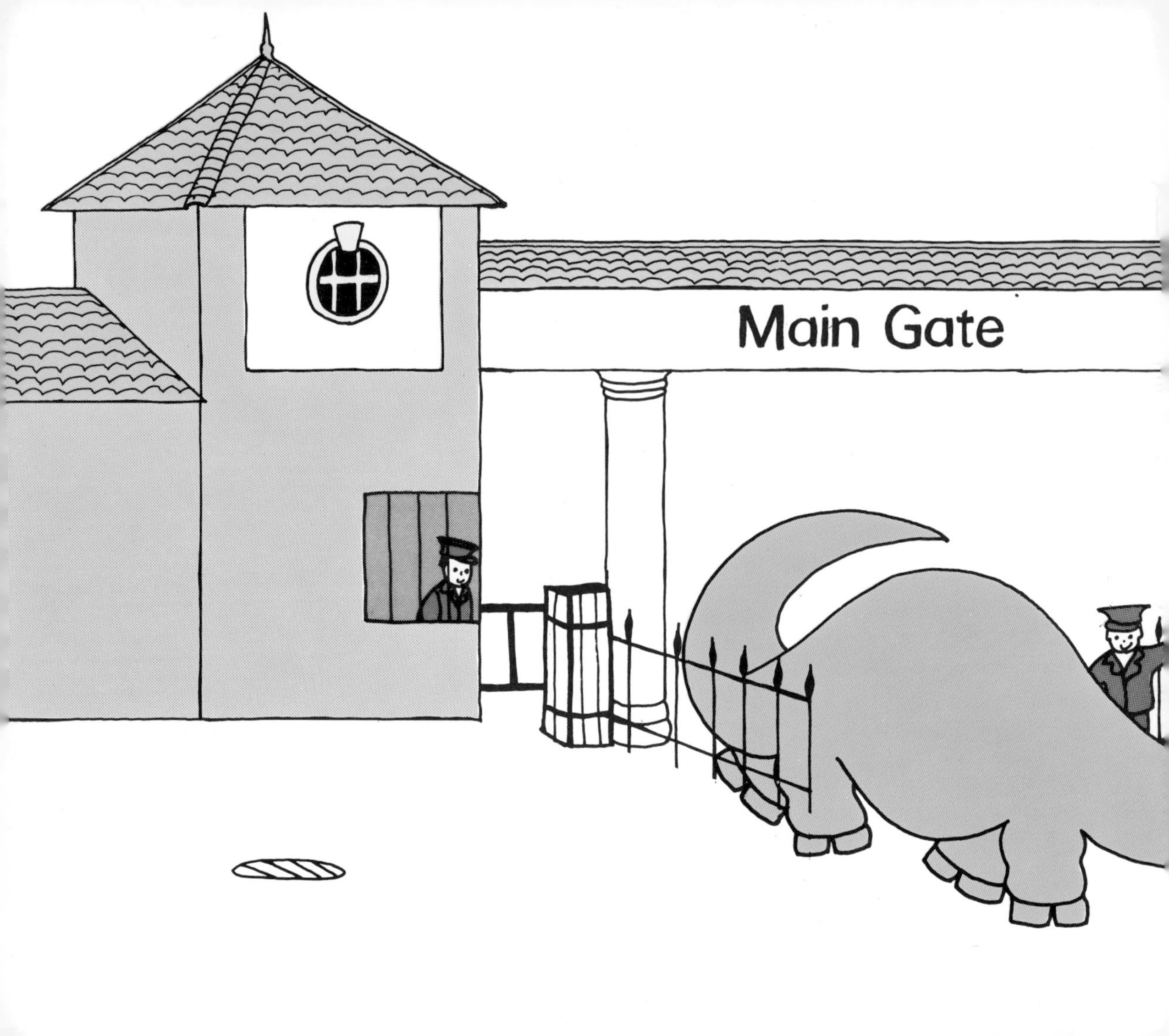
Main Gate

Desmond went to the zoo
to see all the animals.
He paid his money, but he was
too big to get through the turnstile.
They had to open the gate
specially for him.

First he went to see the monkeys.
They ran up and down their tree
and chattered to him.
One of them gave Desmond
a banana.

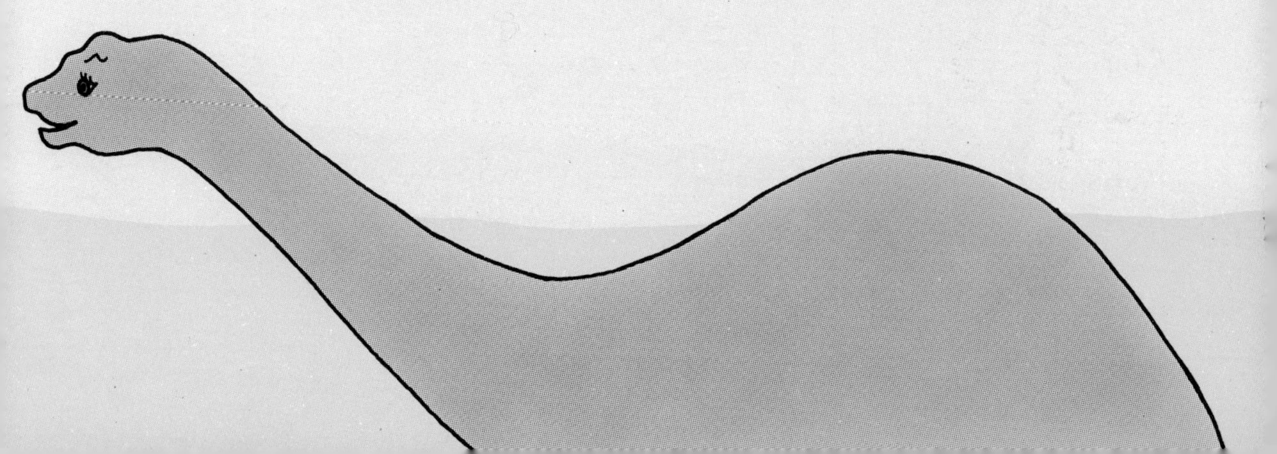

Desmond walked to the elephant house.
The elephants were having a bath.
The keeper was washing them,
and they were washing the keeper !

The lions were dozing in the sun.
They were pleased to see Desmond.
They had been feeling rather bored
and it was fun to have
a friend to talk to.

The sea lions were catching fish thrown to them by their keeper. One of them kept barking for more.

The giraffes lifted their heads
and curled their tongues round
some tasty shoots
growing from the trees.
It must be nice to be so tall
thought Desmond.

Desmond watched the penguins
as they waddled up to their pool
and dived into the water.
They can swim much better
than me, he thought.

Next he went to see a polar bear.
He wondered what it would be like
to live in the cold Arctic
where the bear came from.

Desmond had not noticed,
but he was being followed
by a large crowd of people.

The head keeper hurried up to see
what all the people were looking at.
'Hello Desmond!
Did you know everyone is following you
instead of visiting the other animals?'

Desmond looked round in surprise.

'Please Desmond, will you come
and live with us ?
We will build you a very
comfortable house and give you lots of
lettuces and oranges !'

‘The people just love to talk to you and maybe you could give them rides sometimes — like our camel.’

‘No thank you’, said Desmond.
‘It is kind of you to ask me,
but I would rather be free
to come and go, even if
I don’t have so many lettuces
and oranges.’

The other animals were sorry that
Desmond was not coming to live with them.
'I'll come and see you all again soon'
said Desmond.

Desmond plodded slowly off home.
It had been a nice day
but his feet hurt
after all the walking.